D1621632

"WHAT IS REAL" ASKED THE RABBIT ONE DAY......
" DOES IT MEAN HAVING THINGS THAT BUZZ
INSIDE YOU, AND A STICK OUT HANDLE?"
"REAL ISN'T HOW YOUR'E MADE", SAID THE SKIN HORSE,
"IT'S A THING THAT HAPPENS TO YOU WHEN A CHILD LOVES
YOU FOR A LONG LONG TIME, NOT JUST TO PLAY WITH,
BUT REALLY LOVES YOU, THEN YOU BECOME REAL".
"DOES IT HURT?" ASKED THE RABBIT, "SOMETIMES",
SAID THE SKIN HORSE, FOR HE WAS ALWAYS TRUTHFUL.
"WHEN YOUR'E REAL, YOU DON'T MIND BEING HURT".
" DOES IT HAPPEN ALL AT ONCE, LIKE BEING WOUND UP,"
HE ASKED, "OR BIT BY BIT?".
"IT DOESN'T HAPPEN ALL AT ONCE", SAID THE SKIN HORSE,
"YOU 'BECOME', IT TAKES A LONG TIME, THAT'S WHY IT
DOESN'T HAPPEN TO PEOPLE WHO BREAK EASILY, OR WHO
HAVE SHARP EDGES, OR WHO HAVE TO BE CAREFULLY KEPT.
GENERALLY, BY THE TIME YOU ARE REAL, MOST OF YOUR HAIR
HAS BEEN LOVED OFF AND YOUR EYES DROP OUT AND YOU
GET LOOSE IN THE JOINTS AND VERY SHABBY,
BUT THESE THINGS DON'T MATTER AT ALL, BECAUSE
ONCE YOU ARE REAL, YOU CAN'T BE UGLY, EXEPT TO
PEOPLE WHO DON'T UNDERSTAND."

FROM 'THE VELVETEEN RABBIT'.
by. MARGERY WILLIAMS,

THE SPIRAL CAGE

ISBN 1 85286 222 X

Published by
Titan Books Ltd
58 St Giles High Street
London WC2H 8LH

First edition April 1990
10 9 8 7 6 5 4 3 2 1

AL DAVISON

THE SPIRAL CAGE

DIARY OF AN ASTRAL GYPSY

TITAN BOOKS
LONDON

INTRODUCTION

The first time that I saw the work you are about to read, it was in colour. Dave Gibbons and myself, attending London's Society of Strip Illustrators to talk about our experiences creating *Watchmen*, found ourselves talking to Al Davison and cooing over the hand-coloured version of *The Spiral Cage* that he was prevailed upon to show us. I would dwell at length upon the delicate hues and the sophisticated colour sensibilities that marked every page, except that I wouldn't want anyone to get the impression that the work in question is any the less successful for being in black and white. It's true that, dazzled by the irridescence of the first version I'd seen, I was somewhat apprehensive concerning the prospect of a monochrome interpretation. Such doubts, however, vanished with my first glimpse of the volume in hand. If anything, the black and white presentation demonstrated even more ably the strength of Al's artwork, sturdy and sensitive even without the cosmetic benefits of colour to enhance it. One thing I didn't get a chance to do during that first, necessarily hurried overview was to actually read the thing, something that I have since remedied more than a few times. In the course of these readings and re-readings I've come across a further pleasant revelation: not only does the art stand up perfectly without the exquisite colouring, but the storytelling and substance of *The Spiral Cage* is a match for either.

Let me elaborate upon that: To me, *The Spiral Cage* is an important work upon a couple of levels. Firstly, as the expression of a personal vision and personal experiences, it is clearly a work of the first water. I doubt that anyone could read it without getting a very powerful sense of its protagonist's situation and feelings. The way in which those feelings are articulated, and the tremendously uplifting sense of optimism that they engender would be a tribute to the power of even the most seasoned comics professional, and doubly so to an artist whose first published work is represented by the book in your hands.

Secondly, *The Spiral Cage* is an important addition to the ranks of comic books that strive to break out of the conventions of genre and establish a beach-head of work with genuine human worth and relevance. That Al Davison is a long-time comics fan is evident by the Batman costume his child protagonist is seen wearing. That he has chosen not to slavishly recreate the genre-preferences of his childhood is equally evident, and should be applauded as such.

Many potentially good artists and writers, overjoyed to find themselves actually working in comics of any kind, allow themselves to become hidebound and institutionalized in the traditions of juvenile superhero comics, eventually becoming unable to imagine working in any other area. Speaking as someone who has worked fairly well within the tried and tested genres of superheroes and science fiction and has reaped the obvious financial benefits of such a safe and conventional path, I have nothing but the deepest admiration for those, like Al, who have had the courage to their marques so far beyond the rigid perimeters of the comic book mainstream. Of course, the main risk of staking out such untrodden creative areas is a financial one; traditionally, a comic fan market weaned upon superheroes has been reluctant to try out any fare that varied too much from the diet that they were used to. I may be being optimistic, but this may not always be the case.

Comic fans themselves are changing, their tastes gradually widening. This year they can accept comics with superheroes so strange and different that they hardly seem to be superheroes at all. Next year, who knows? Perhaps the fan audience will actually be able to tolerate, en masse, the idea of comics without a single cape or mask in sight. Of course, the long-time traditional comic fan market is not the only audience we have to consider; I don't know how the situation stands in America, but in this country comic shops have doubled or trebled their flow of customers over the last couple of years, largely due to the sudden attention being paid to comics by the media in the wake of *Dark Knight, Maus*, and so on. This trend would indicate that there exists out there an audience potentially twice as large as our existing one. More importantly, since this audience would seem not to have the same long-term grounding in conventional comic lore, it may be assumed that after a while they'll get tired of seeing unusual slants upon the clichés of the superhero genre and start looking for more varied and sustaining fare. We'd better hope that such fare is there and available for them, otherwise they may simply wander away again, back to their VCRs and their Walkmans. In this last respect, it is the existence of books like *The Spiral Cage* that offers a real ray of hope for the future of the medium.

Beautifully drawn and written, expertly told, the story contained within these pages manages to talk about things that many people still find it difficult to talk or think about, and to do so in a way that is at once accessible, entertaining and elevating. By addressing the world upon the level of the all-too-human rather than that of the unreachably superhuman it manages to say something for all of us, able and otherwise, seemingly within our own bodies and circumstances; apparently locked forever within the inescapable spiral cage of our own DNA. Within the discipline of his craft and the patience of his work within these pages, Al Davison seems to have found a key to the lock of his own cage.

Try it. Who knows? Maybe it'll fit yours too.

ALAN MOORE
Northampton, May 1988

For
Ellen and Frank Davison, my parents.
& Susan Davison, my sister,
for their courage;
Emily Wilding Davison, my great aunt,
for a lifetime of inspiration;
my doctors, teachers, physios etc
who made the most of a bad job . . .
and, last, but never least,
nurses everywhere.

Acknowledgments

Ann Muxworthy, Integrated Resources Project, Tyneside Free Press, Prontaprint, Metro-Repro, Alison Little, Deni Loubert, Bryan Talbot, Mr and Mrs Will Eisner, Alan Moore and Dave Gibbons.

Special thanks

Annie, Chris, Emily and Matt Moir; Carol and Brian and family; the very odd people behind the counter at Timeslip; Iris Penny and family and friends at the Book House; Matthew and Jenny; Suzi Varty; Neil Gaiman; the *A1* crew; John Bolton; *Crisis;* Jock Garriock; Jnr Print Outfit; everyone in NSUK, especially North Tyne District; Jack and Lucy Rickards and family; Sheena Dickson; Denise and Paul and family; *Deadline*, Linda Barron; Jo Lane; Annette Whitelaw; Paula McKennell; Celia Webb; Karen Thomas; Robyn Hayter; Laura Caan; Claire; Mr and Mrs McAllister; Becky and Debbie; Kathy and Sarah; Catherine Appleby; Charlie Cattell; Helen White; Fiona and Judith; Louise C Treanor; Sarah Gerhard; Carol and husband; Angela Foley; Jacqueline Thomson; Kate; Jackie; Jemima Gladwell; V Bayliss, Mal and Helen; Heidi, Breyna and the Anthill Runaways; Louise Williams; Lindsy; Sharon; Karen; Anna; Diane Walker; Robert Pool; Louise and John; Fiona (thanks for the proof reading); Bill Sienkiewicz; Frank Miller; Lynn Varley; Carl Potts; Len Wein; the 'Stormy Monday' crew; Sean Bean; Fred Bear Video; the Space Pirates; Gary Groth; Dave Sim; Gerhard; Trina Robbins; Myra Hancock; Seth; Phil Elliot; Paul Gravett; Cat Yronewode; Janet and Terry and family; Charles and Linda; Dan Day; Dave Darrigo; R.G. Taylor; William Leong; Roger; Anna Lenaghen; Debbie Tuck; and a big hug to Lisa Atkinson and all my friends I don't have room to mention here.

Trying to realise memories, memories forgotten, that still cling, images unseen, yet vivid in the shadows,.... waiting, the fascination ...
            the fear...
                as with shadows,
sometimes,
        comes from what they hide, rather than what they reveal.....

but sometimes a memory unravelled, can be an excorcist, freeing you to live in the "now" rather than the "then"
    To move forward,
An occurrence in life, is only an "experience", once your life has acknowledged it,
    Some such occurrences demand to be acknowledged and cling desperately,

waiting to be freed.. recalled, remembered....

I was born with severe, spina-Bifida, a condition, which leaves you paralysed from the waist down., and can also leave you with brain damage first "they" said I wouldn't Live.. then they said I shouldn't live... my parents disagreed.

First time around.. again.

BIRTH PAINS!

"LIFE IS THE MOST PRECIOUS OF
ALL TREASURES.
EVEN ONE EXTRA DAY OF LIFE
IS WORTH MORE THAN TEN MILLION
RYO OF GOLD."

NICHIREN DAISHONIN
'ON PROLONGING LIFE'.
MAJ. WRITINGS, VOL 1.

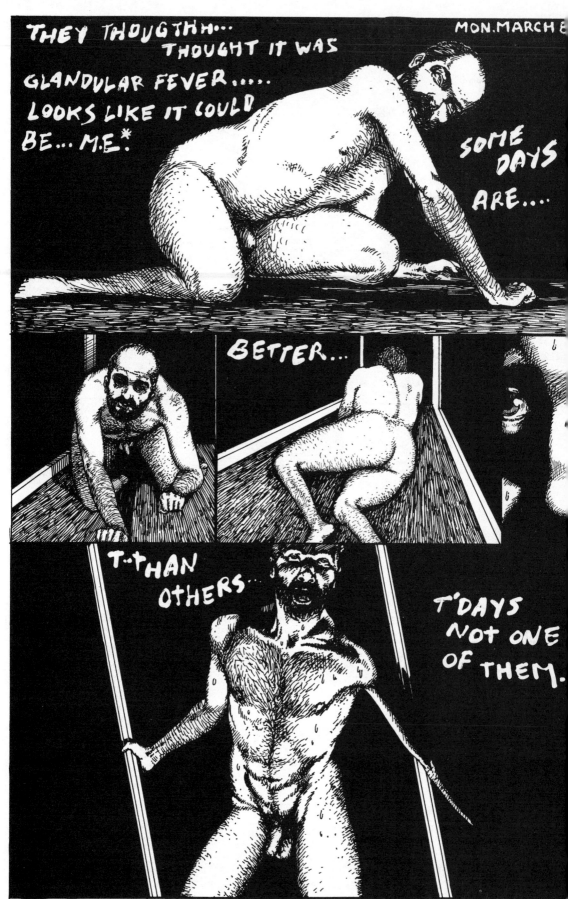

* MYALGIC ENCEPHOLOMYELITIS, ALSO KNOWN AS, POST VIRAL FATIGUE SYNDROME.

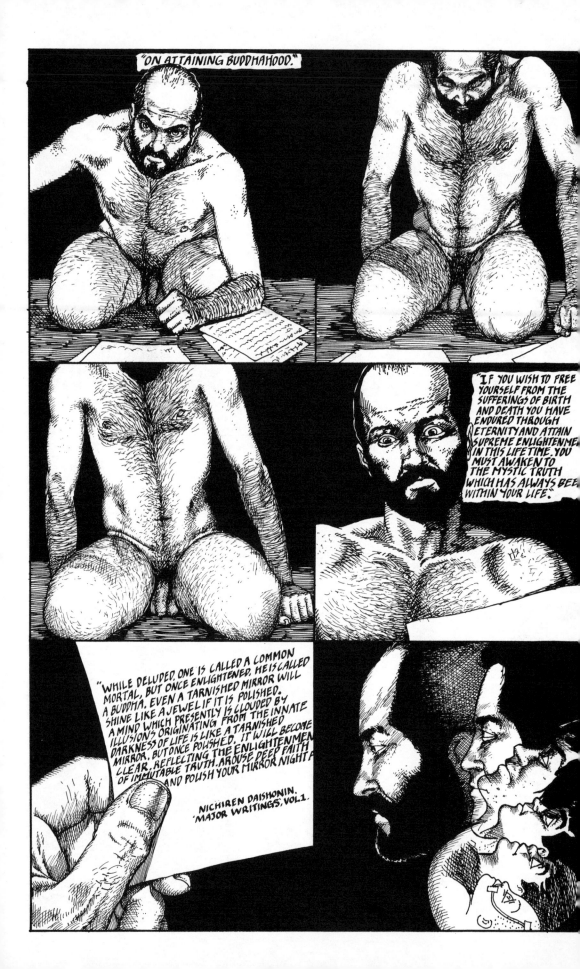

16.1.1960.

IT'S A BOY......

Jan 17th 1960

SPINA BIFIDA

Dislocation of left hip caused by malformation of the lateral surface of the iliac bone i.e. no deep excavation of socket for the head of the femur to connect with.

We can't tell as of yet if the upper spine is affected so we have to insert a valve in case of fluid pressure on the brain. It will dissolve in a few years if it is not needed. Both femur, fibula and tibia of both legs are . . .

severely distorted. Both femurs are such that at the moment we cannot open the legs. We should be able to rectify this to a degree, enough at least for the mother to dress him . . .

and change him etc. His ankles are also fused (the talus and the two malleoli) preventing any flexing of the feet...it is of course unlikely he could flex his feet even without this problem, as in such severe cases as this he will be paralysed from the waist down . . .

Our first job is to cover the open wound at the base of the spine which exposes the lower vertebrae and Coccyx. A usual characteristic of spina bifida, we will graft skin taken from the shin to cover the wound. Two years' minimum recovery from this operation.

We can't even say he will survive this first operation. He is literally a 'hopeless case', this is not meaning to sound defeatist, but there is little hope. His parents are adamant, however, to proceed no matter what, against my advice. So we must do what we can . . .

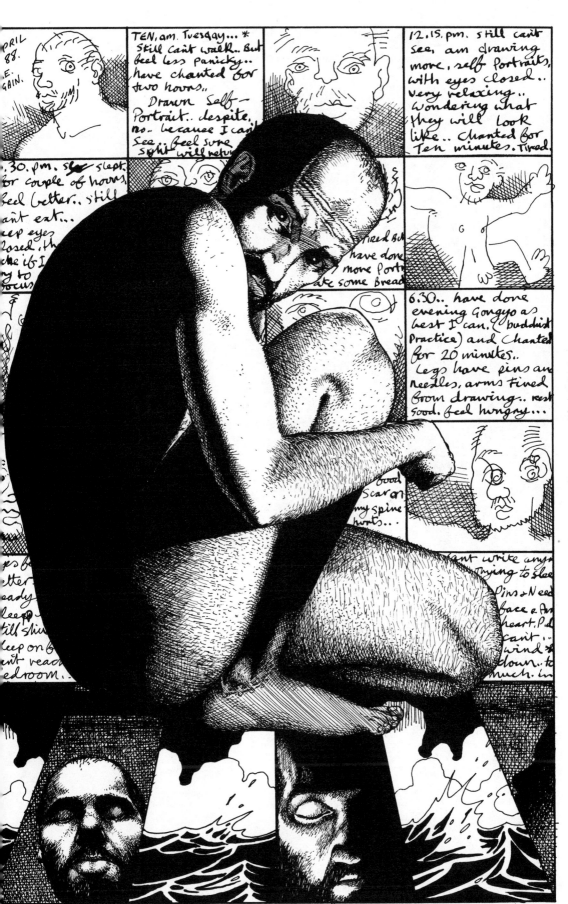

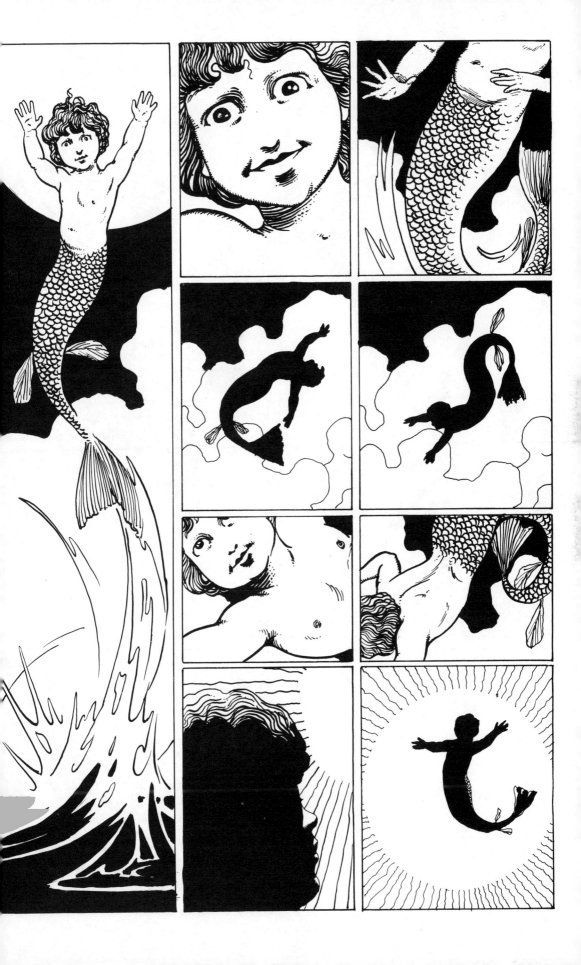

HE WILL NOT REQUIRE MEDKATION, JUST... KEEP AN EYE ON HIM, AND REPORT ANY CHANGE. OK.

YES SISTER, DOES HE... SLEEP ALL NIGHT, NORMALLY?

MOSTLY. HE GIGGLES... ALOT, BETTER THAN CRYING..

SO DON'T BE TO... WORRIED IF HE WAKES UP LAUGHING WE'VE GOTTEN USED TO HIM, FUNNY KID!...

BARELY ALIVE AND HE CAN'T STOP LAUGHING STILL... HE IS ALIVE, SO MAYBE....

MAYBE THAT IS REASON ENOUGH ... FOR NOW..... OH YES, IF YOU WANT TO ATTRACT HIS...

ATTENTION.. HE ANSWER

TO... SMILER..!.

?

WHEEEEEE

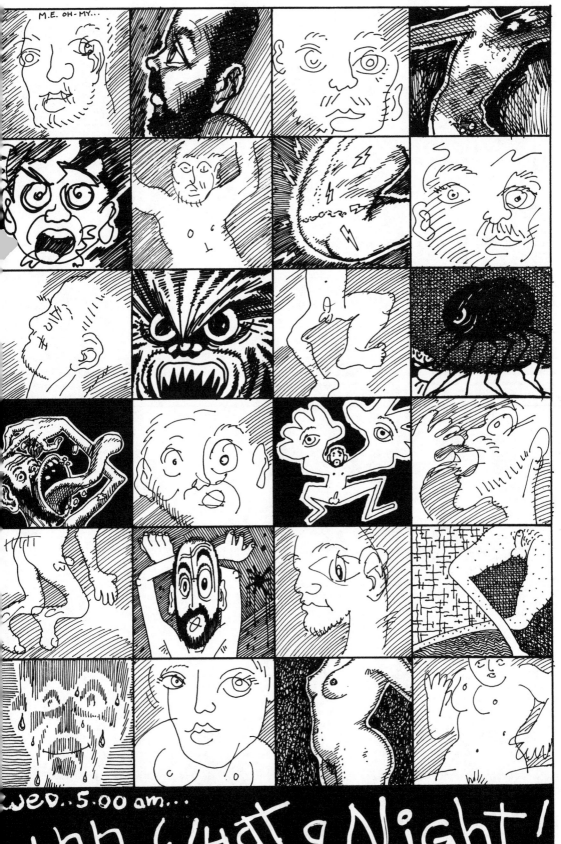

A FOUR MILE JOURNEY, TO LEAVE MY SISTER WITH AUNTIE SUSIE, WHILE MY MAM TOOK ME TO HOSPITAL. EIGHT MILES ON THE BUS TO THE TOWN, CHANGE BUSES, FOUR MILES TO THE HOSPITAL*, IN GATESHEAD..... AND BACK AGAIN. MY MAM MADE THIS JOURNEY EVERY DAY FOR... NEARLY THREE YEARS. SOMETIMES TWICE A DAY WHEN I WAS HAVING OPERATIONS.
*EVERY OTHER DAY IT WOULD BE TO THE GREENFIELDS CLINIC, FOR PHYSIO, ALSO IN GATESHEAD,

EVERYBODY lives in Hospital till THEY HAVE LOTS of operations so they can WALK.

When You are 5 or [6] You go To a school full of People who sti[ll] Cant WaLK and aRe i[n] Wheelchairs...

Some can walk.. But they have Holes In there Hearts or Asthma..

← BOY ON ASTHMA BED.

Some PeoPLE ARE SCARED ALOt AND tHey cry

I LiKe LeaRNi[ng] To WALK.

I START SCHOOL NEXt year. I CAN reaD I Learned in the Ambulance every DAY

AMBULANCE

PeoPle on TeLevis[ion] Dont Have HoLes in Their heart or Asth[ma] And they can wa[lk]

BANG

BUT THEY ARENt ReAL.

TEACHERS and Doctors CAN WALK BUt THEY are OLD.

well almost......

first steps (mark II)....

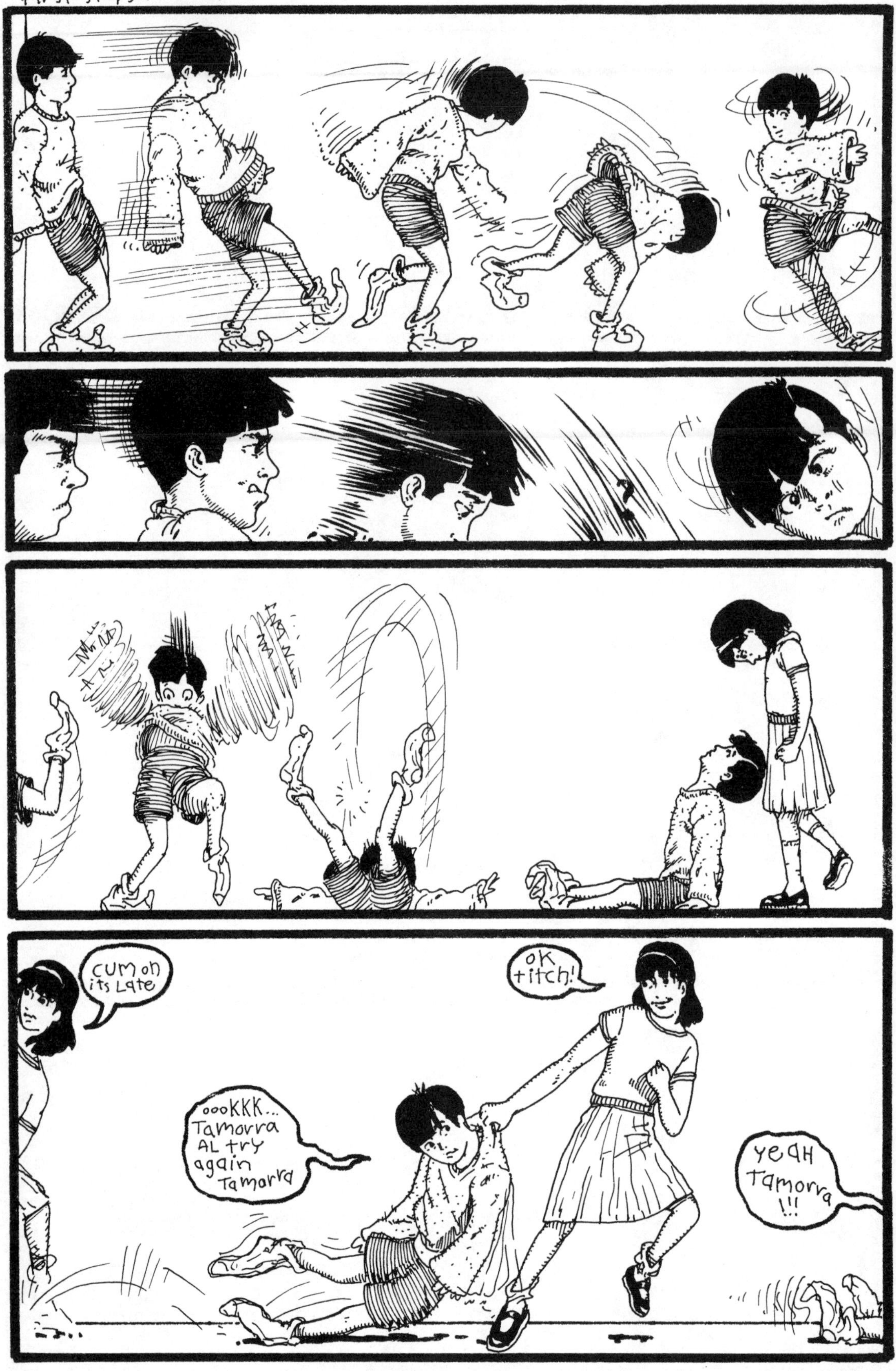

EVEN THOUGH MR MIDGLEY WAS SO ENCOURAGING, HE HAD
EVENTUALLY TO ADMIT TO MY MOTHER THAT HE FELT SURE
THAT I WOULD NEVER WALK... THOUGH HE NEVER TOLD ME OF
HIS DOUBTS... AND I NEVER SUSPECTED HE EVEN HAD ANY, SO THE
DAY I TOOK MY FIRST SIX STEPS... I WASN'T ABLE TO UNDERSTAND
THE SIGNIFICANCE OF ALL THE TEARS THAT WERE SHED.... AND
WHAT A SIGNIFICANT DINT I HAD MADE IN MY SPIRAL CAGE.
I JUST SAID." DAT WUZ A GWAIT TWICK, CAN A DO IT AGAIN EH? CAN A?"...

Seeking Spirit!

"IF YOU DO NOT QUESTION
AND RESOLVE DOUBTS,
YOU CANNOT DISPEL THE DARK
CLOUDS OF ILLUSION.......
...... ASK ANY QUESTIONS YOU LIKE".

NICHIREN DAISHONIN
'LETTER TO NIIKE'.
MAJ. WRITINGS, VOL 1.

NOV. 1964.

RESTING?! AT HOME, SHORTLY AFTER MY 14th OPERATION. STILL PARALYSED FROM THE WAIST DOWN.

YAAAAAHOOOOOOOOOOOOOOOOOOOOO... HIC!! GIGGLE.......... HE HEEEE.

KARMA?

MM... WELL LET'S SEE... OK.. LET'S SAY IN YOUR PREVIOUS LIFE, YOU WERE AN ARTIST. BUT MAYBE YOU BECAME COMPLACENT. FOR EXAMPLE A COURT PAINTER JUST PAINTING WHAT THE..

KING OR QUEEN WANTED, NOT STRETCHING YOURSELF AT ALL... THEN MAYBE YOU WOULD BE BORN AGAIN...

WITH 'SPINA-BIFIDA, IN ORDER TO GIVE YOU THE MEANS TO CHALLENGE YOUR COMPLACENCY... OF COURSE... IT WOULD STILL BE UP TO YOU WHETHER OR NOT YOU TOOK UP THE CHALLENGE.

LIVE AT THE COOPERA
III JAZZOWACKY...
III R.D.B. SPITFIRES...
III SEBROD DIVE...

YES, BUT SIMPLY PUT IT'S THE ACCUMULATION OF ALL THE EFFECTS FROM THE CAUSES YOU HAVE MADE.

...FROM THE CAUSES YOU HAVE EVER MADE" CATHERINE SAID... BUT CHARLIE ALSO SAID HE THOUGHT HIS EXAMPLE MIGHT BE MISLEADING... IT SOUNDED A BIT LIKE HE WAS SAYING.....

Llandudno
4th July 89.

THAT, SOMEHOW A CONSCIOUS DECISION WAS INVOLVED.... LIKE GOD DECIDING YOU NEEDED TO LEARN A LESSON, RATHER THAN IT BEING.......

"A NATURAL LAW. LIKE GRAVITY, STRAIGHT FORWARD CAUSE AND EFFECT... ANYWAY THAT WAS MY FIRST INTRO-DUCTION TO THE CONCEPT OF 'KARMA'... BACK THEN... THAT MUST HAVE BEEN... WELL.. MM.. 1980/81.. I THINK IT WAS BEFORE I CAME ACROSS 'NICHIREN SHOSHU,' BUDDHISM, ANYWAY,...... BUT BETWEEN THEN AND MY DISCOVERING BUDDHISM, I FOUND VARIOUS.. DIFFERENT EXPLANATIONS OF KARMA.... SOME, WELL... THEY SEEMED TO BE INDICATING THAT "KARMA".... WAS A FIXED FATE IN THE HANDS OF SOME DEITY, OR GOD... OTHERS... THAT YOU COULD ONLY CHANGE YOUR KARMA IF YOU WERE A PRIEST AND THAT AS A LAY PERSON

YOUR ONLY HOPE WAS TO SUPPORT THE PRIESTHOOD IN THE HOPE THAT YOU WOULD BE RE-BORN INTO A GOOD FAMILY AND BECOME A PRIEST IN YOUR NEXT LIFE.... OR ANOTHER VERSION STATES...

YOU COULD CHANGE, BUT ONLY AFTER ENDLESS LIFE TIMES, EONS OF COUNTLESS AUSTERITIES, OR MAYBE BY THE GRACE OF GOD.". " DID CATHERINE AND CHARLIE BELIEVE THAT KARMA COULD BE CHANGED IN THIS LIFE TIME?" "OH YES, BUT THEY ADMIT THAT THE PRACTICE THEY USE WOULD PROBABLY ONLY BE OF USE TO A SMALL PERCENTAGE OF PEOPLE. ITS NOT FOR EVERYONE. AND THAT THIS BUDDHISM, IS MORE PRACTICAL, A LOT LESS OBSCURE, BUT THATS WHAT I LIKED ABOUT IT, ITS SIMPLICITY, NO MESSING ABOUT, OF COURSE IT ISN'T EASY TO UNDERSTAND. BUT YOU START BY DOING IT, SEEING IF IT WORKS, NO BLIND FAITH... YOUR UNDERSTANDING COMES FROM EXPERIENCING IT, NOT JUST THEORY, SPEAKING OF WHICH, ENOUGH THEORY... TIME FOR SOME ACTION." "YEAH, WELL I WOULD LIKE TO 'EXPERIENCE, SOME FOOD... I'M STARVING... LETS FIND SUSAN AND HAZEL, AND GET LUNCH..."

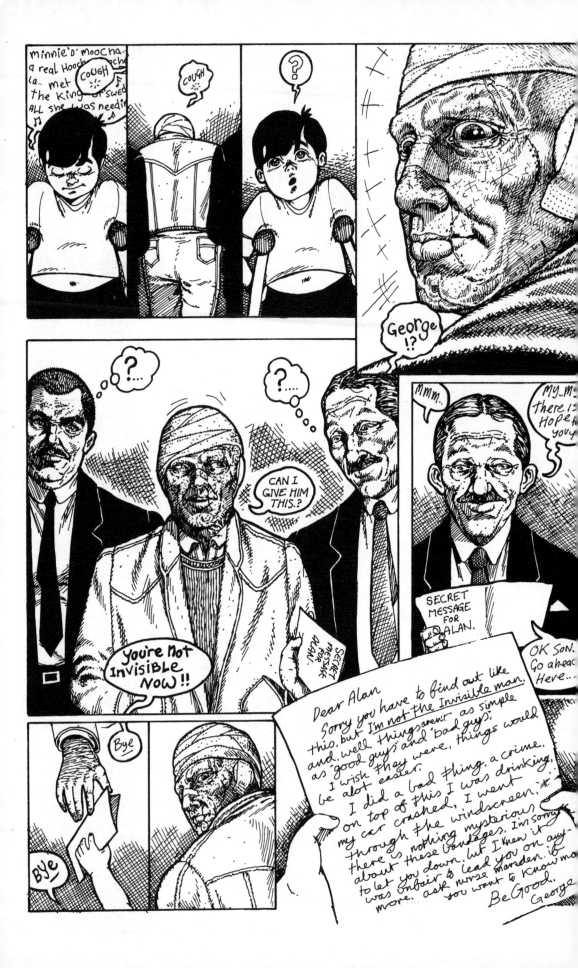

"YOU OFFERED THIS SWORD TO THE LOTUS SUTRA, WHILE YOU WORE IT AT YOUR SIDE IT WAS AN EVIL SWORD, BUT NOW IT HAS BEEN OFFERED TO THE BUDDHA, IT HAS BECOME A SWORD FOR GOOD,........ IN THE NEXT LIFE YOU SHOULD USE THIS SWORD AS YOUR WALKING STICK".

NICHIREN DAISHONIN.
'THE SWORDS OF GOOD AND EVIL'.
MAJ. WRITINGS, VOL. 1.

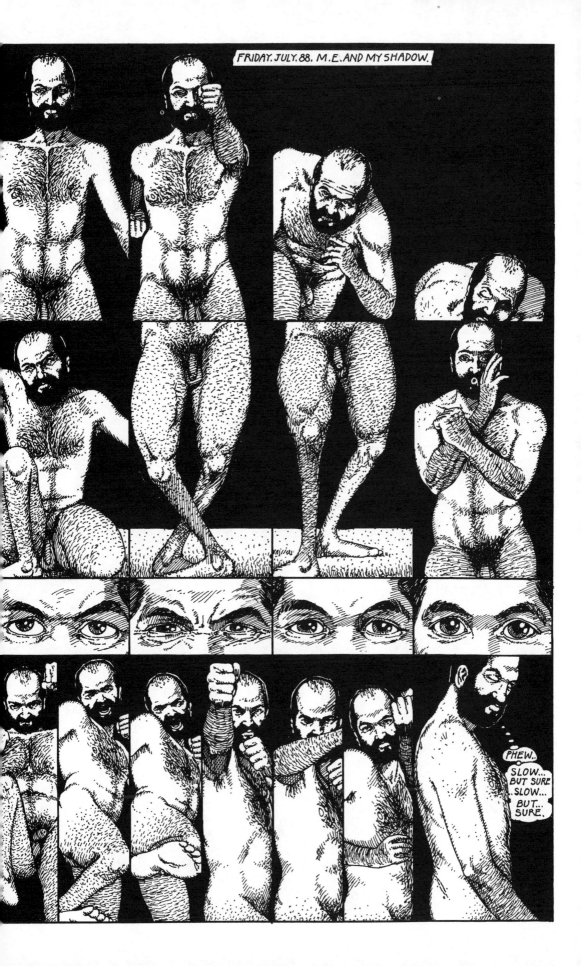

IT'S THE SORT OF STUNT I SAW IN THE 'KUNG-FU' MOVIES ALL THE TIME. HERO KICKS BAD GUY OFF BIKE... THEN DANCES THE NIGHT... AWAY WITH A BEAUTIFUL WOMAN. EXCEPT HE DIDN'T SPEND THE NEXT MONTH WITH GROIN STRAIN AND DIARRHOEA! THE PEOPLE WHOSE CAR ENDED UP ON VERY INTIMATE TERMS WITH A CERTAIN BIKE, OFFERED TO SORT THINGS OUT.. BUT THEY SUGGESTED I RUN IN CASE HIS MATES RETURNED.. THEY PROMISED TO EXPLAIN TO THE POLICE. I WAS TERRIFIED IN CASE MY PARENTS FOUND OUT, FUNNY THO' HOW I COULD NEVER DO THAT KICK IN THE KARATE CLASS. AND HAVE NEVER MANAGED IT SINCE...

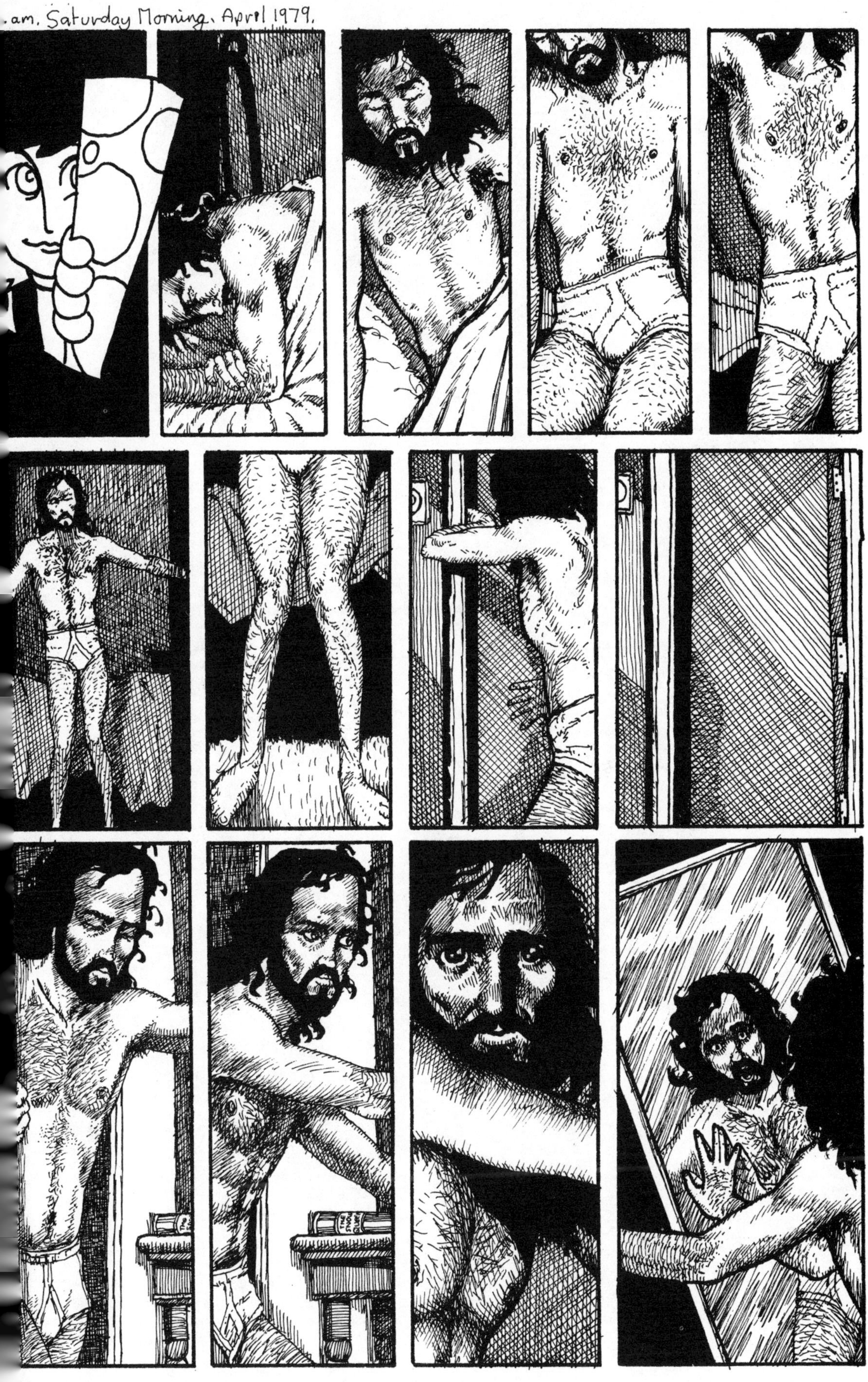
.am. Saturday Morning. April 1979.

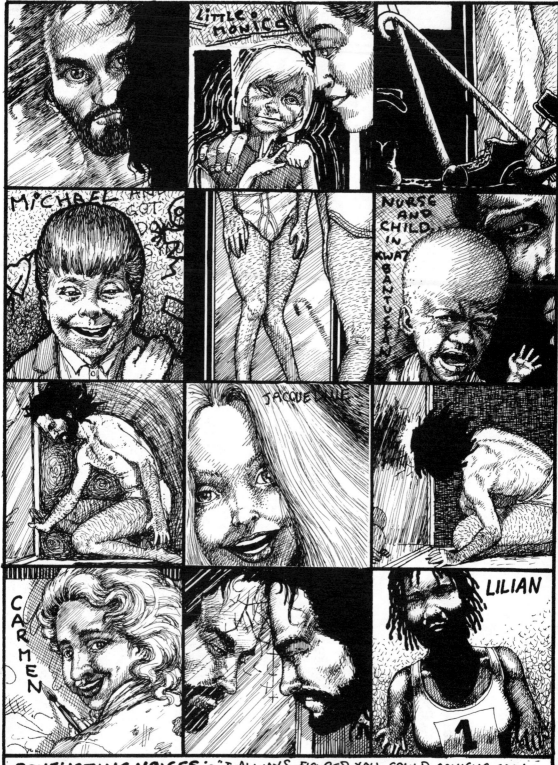

CONFLICTING VOICES :- "I ALWAYS FIGURED YOU.. COULD ACHIEVE ANY-thing." (LAURA).. "YOU, BOY, HAVE IDEAS ABOVE YOUR STATION... WALK.. INDEED! (PHYSIOTHERAPIST). "CALIPERS ..ARE LIKE TAKING A CAGE with you wherever you go... I hate cages." (my own voice Age 4½). "you can't Avoid your limitations Boy." (Doctor). You Have to accept your limitations, but only Long enough to figure out how to overcome them. (KARATE TEACHER)

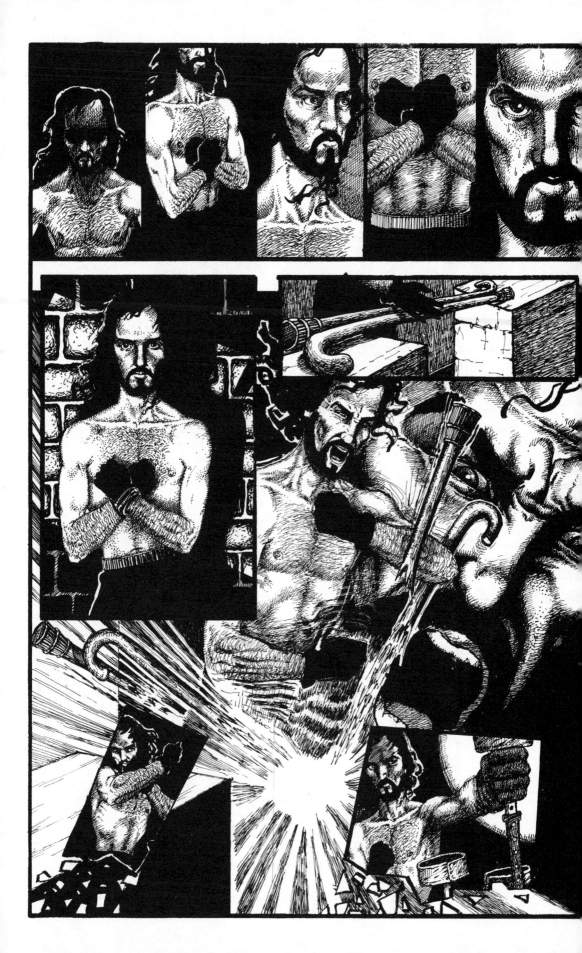

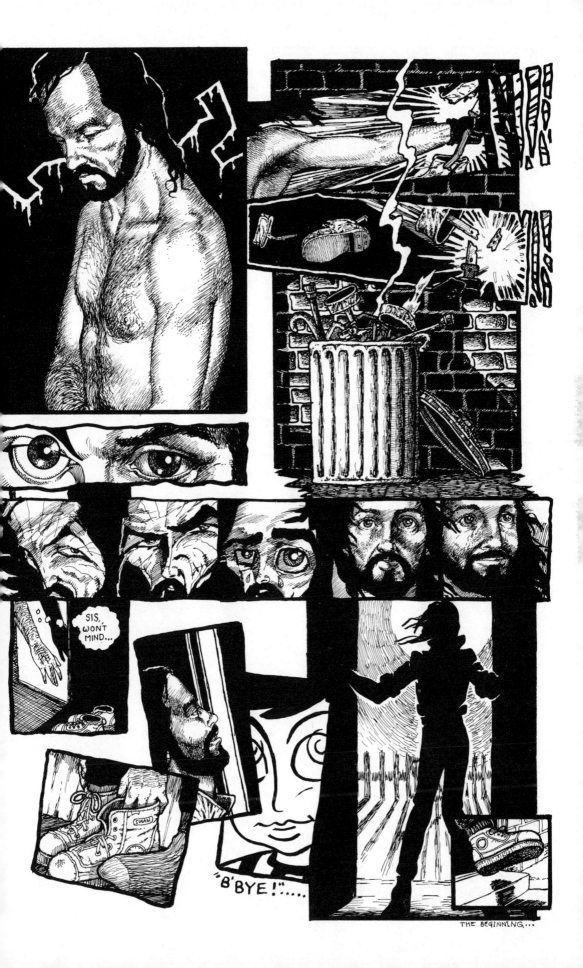

Chapter 4.

Dream Weaving.

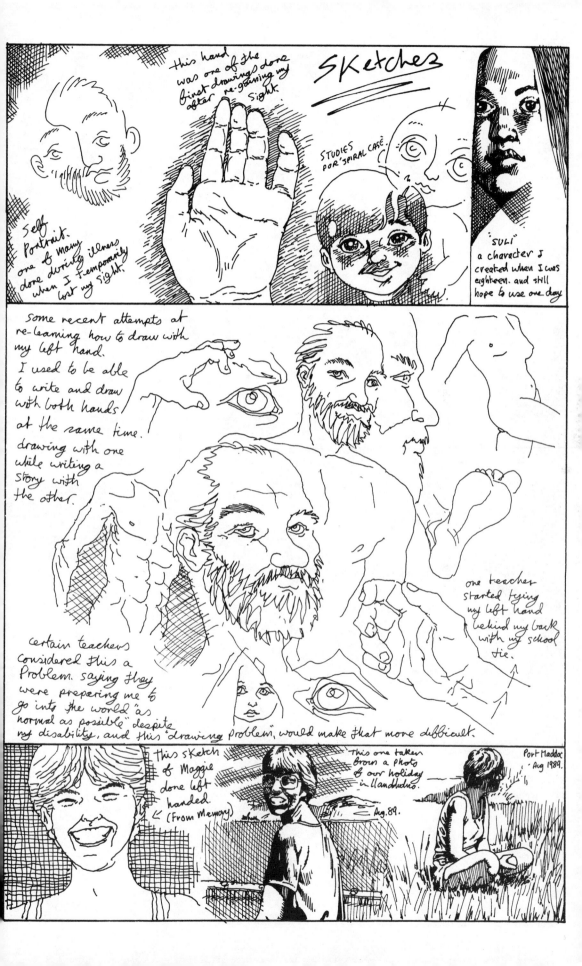

this hand of the first drawings done after re-gaining my sight.

Sketches

Self Portrait. one of many done during illness when I temporarily lost my sight.

STUDIES FOR 'SPIRAL CASE'

'SULI' a character I created when I was eighteen. and still hope to use one day

some recent attempts at re-learning how to draw with my left hand. I used to be able to write and draw with both hands at the same time. drawing with one while writing a story with the other.

certain teachers considered this a problem. saying they were preparing me to go into the world "as normal as possible" despite my disability, and this 'drawing problem' would make that more difficult.

one teacher started tying my left hand behind my back with my school tie.

this sketch of Maggie done left handed. (From Memory)

this one taken from a photo of our holiday in Llandudno. — Aug.89.

Port Maddoc. Aug 1989.

SEPT 89

MAM (AGE.69)

ALAN.

EARLY SELF-PORTRAIT.

SUSAN.
"IRON FIST"
DAVISON

my SISTER.
(AGE.30)

NELLIE 'EVIL KNIEVEL' DAVISON. now in a wheelchair after a stroke, and several heart attacks, has taught my dad, everything he knows about how not to drive an electric wheelchair.

SUSAN, was born with 'cerebral palsy', and also has 'epilepsy', the cerebral palsy' has left susan, with a partially paralysed left hand and leg., as well as learning difficulties but she lives independantly, in her flat, she also has won 'one hundred and nine medals in Athletics. (NATIONAL DISABLED GAMES). in just over two years, SIXTY THREE, GOLD, THIRTY NINE SILVER, seven, BRONZE. in Javelin, shot put, Discus, swimming, running... etc etc... etc...

SEPT 89.

Dad (Age. 70.)

FRANK 'MAD MAX' DAVISON.
he traded in his car after several heart attacks, a stroke, and amputation of his right leg, he now has an electric tri-cycle, with which he still manages, to terrify, pedestrians and drivers alike, (not to mention us) he delights in joining the traffic, whilst apparently crossing the road, unfortunately his average speed is about 2.mph, which has an interesting effect on traffic flow, (well that's a polite way of putting it.) he still plays a mean game of lawn bowls, and still paints scenery, albeit from postcards.. these days.

my Bedroom

Some family sKetches

The house we lived in, till my mam had a stroke, I then moved into a flat so they could get a bungalow, my mum is now in care as she requires 24 hour a day care, my dad is still in the bungalow.

! I don't want to remember that... not now... not now....

NO

NO!

N THE NN. NOT JENNY
BRIDGE THINKING OF JENNY NO NO

THINK OF GINA SMILING
YES....

GONE

CAN'T SEE HER

Just see myself... walking to Jenny's house, its cold. Back then...

SHE MIGHT BE WITH HIM..." SORRY I'M BUSY"..."I'VE GOT COMPANY"..OR "WE ARE JU
GOING OUT." SHE SAID SHE STILL WANTED ME TO BE FRIENDS, "I DON'T WANT
THINGS TO CHANGE". SHE SAID. SO WHY DO I GO THROUGH THIS EVERY TIME I GO
..TO SEE HER. MAYBE SHE IS SEEING SOMEONE, MAYBE NOT... BUT I CAN'T THINK..A.
.AB.. ABOUT IT... IT INTRUDES EVERYWHERE... W.. WHATEVER WE DO.. OR..TALK..AB..
..ABOUT... WITH THOSE THOUGHTS, FEELINGS, CREEPING IN ...E..EATING AWAY...

ALL THE WAY ON THE BUS, THIS WALK TO THE HOUSE, HEAR NOW..E.. EATING ..
EATING..AWAY... ALMOST HOPE SHE ISN'T IN.. YET THE DISAPPOINTMENT STILL.
SURPRISES ME, IT JOINS THE FEAST, WITH FEAR, ANGER 'TIL ONLY...
THE EMPTY HUNGER REMAINS, THE HUNGER OF LOVE, THE ONLY THING LEFT
..UNFED... YET IT SURVIVES SOMEHOW.... THEN LEAVING .. I SEE HIM ...

the scarecrow is Dancing!

BUS STOP

he scarecrow......

AUTUMN 1964.

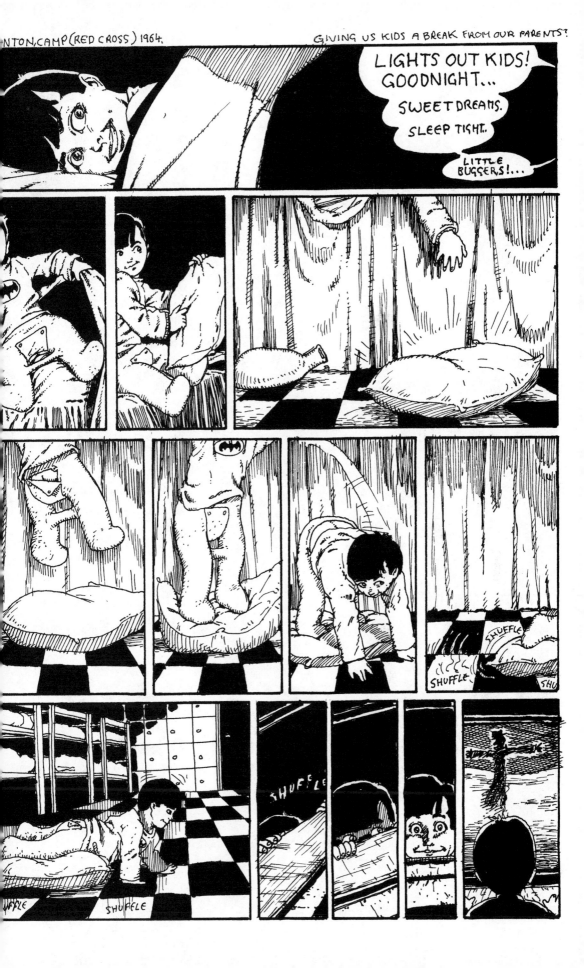

VISIONS:- AGE 3½.

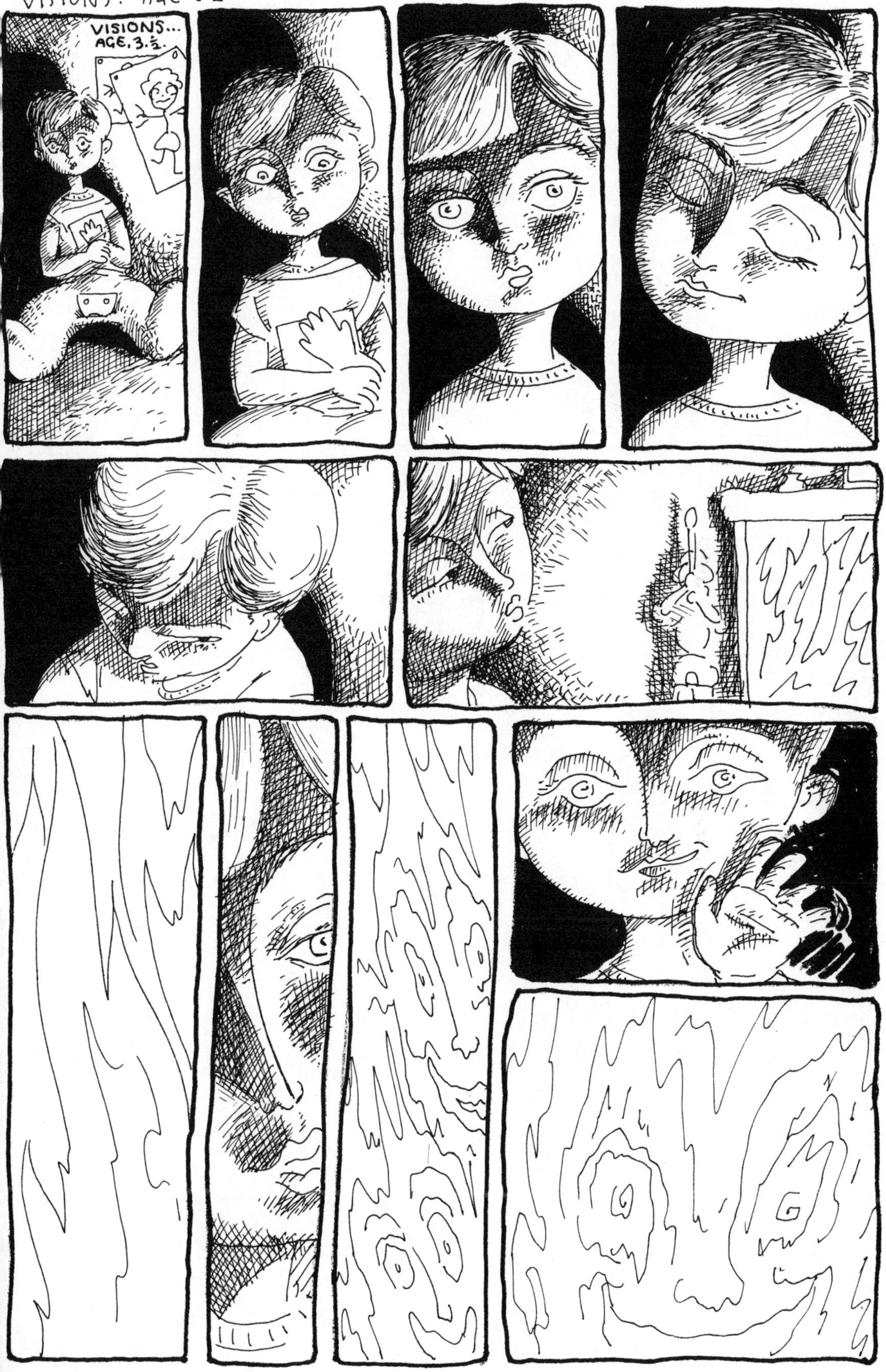

AGE 3½...

THIS WON'T HURT....

A BIT.....

JUST RELAX.

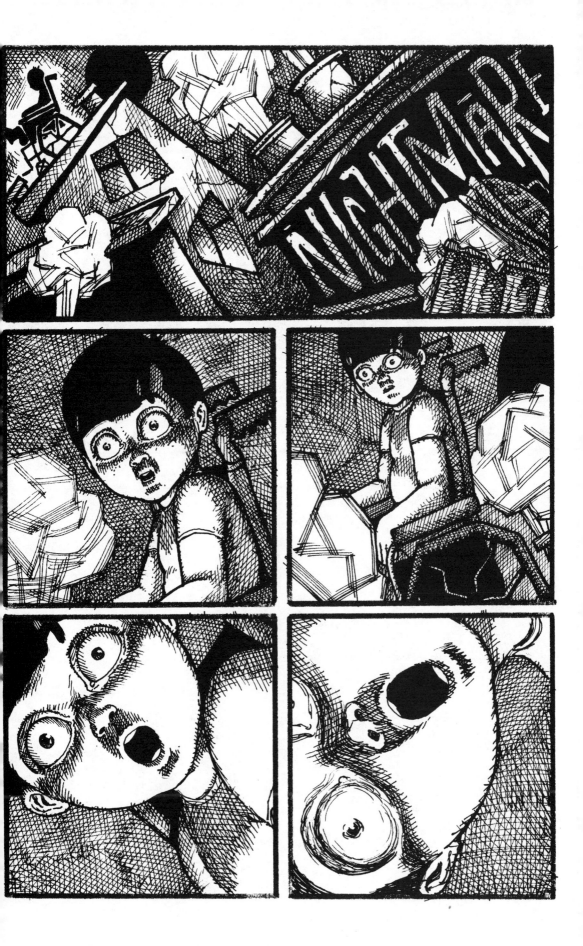

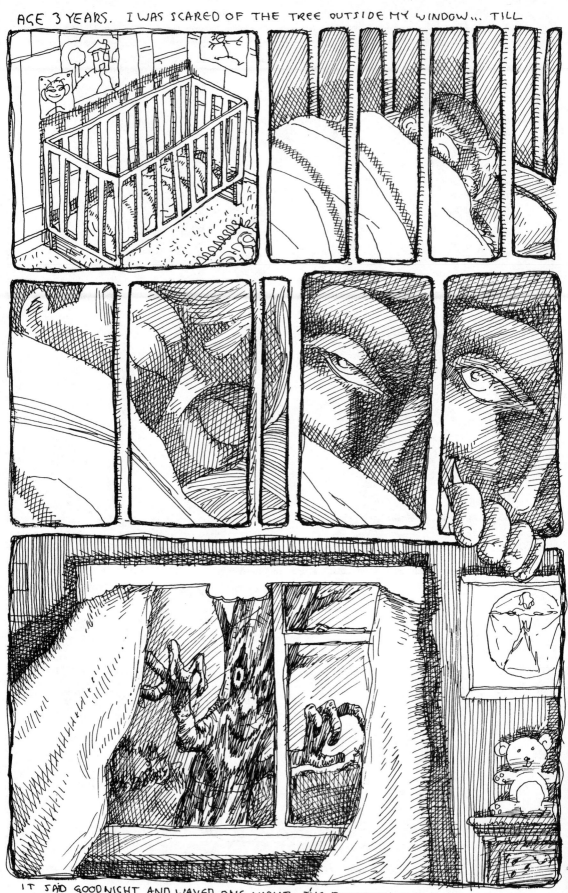

IT SAID GOODNIGHT AND WAVED ONE NIGHT... I'VE FORGOTTEN THE POEM I WROTE, BUT I REMEMBER THE TREE.

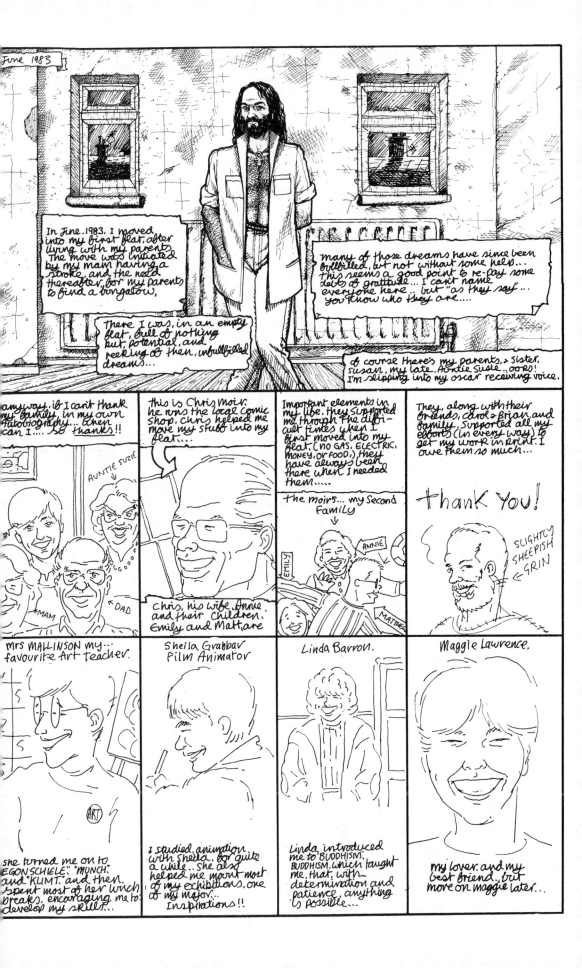

June 1983

In June, 1983, I moved into my first flat, after living with my parents. The move was initiated by my mum having a stroke, and the need thereafter, for my parents to find a bungalow.

many of those dreams have since been fullfilled, but not without some help... this seems a good point to re-pay some debts of gratitude... I can't name everyone here... but "as they say"... you know who they are....

There I was, in an empty flat, full of nothing but potential, and reeking of then, unfulfilled dreams...

of course there's my parents, & sister, susan, my late, Auntie Susie... ooPS! I'm slipping into my oscar receiving voice.

---

anyway, if I can't thank my family, in my own autobiography... when can I..... so thanks!!

AUNTIE SUZIE
MAM
DAD

---

this is Chris Moir. he runs the local comic shop. Chris helped me move my stuff into my flat....

Chris, his wife, Annie and their children, Emily and Matt, are

---

Important elements in my life. they supported me through the difficult times when I first moved into my flat. (no gas, electric, money, or food.) they have always been there when I needed them.....

the moir's... my Second Family

EMILY ANNIE MATHEW

They, along with their friends, carol & brian, and family, supported all my efforts (in every way) to get my work in print. I owe them so much...

thank you!

SLIGHTLY SHEEPISH GRIN

---

mrs MALLINSON my... favourite Art teacher.

ART

she turned me on to EGON SCHIELE; "MUNCH". and "KLIMT". and then spent most of her lunch breaks, encouraging me to develop my skills...

Sheila Grabbar Film Animator

I studied animation with Sheila, for quite a while... she also helped me mount most of my exhibitions, one of my major... Inspirations!!

Linda Barron.

Linda introduced me to BUDDHISM, BUDDHISM, which taught me, that, with determination and patience, anything is possible...

Maggie Lawrence,

my lover, and my best friend... but more on maggie later...

mirror without a reflection.

ALL YOU NeeD IS......

"MORE VALUABLE THAN TREASURES
IN A STOREHOUSE, ARE THE TREASURES
OF THE BODY, AND THE TREASURES
OF THE HEART ARE THE MOST
VALUABLE OF ALL.
FROM THE TIME YOU READ THIS LETTER
ON, STRIVE TO ACCUMULATE TREASURES
OF THE HEART."
NICHIREN DAISHONIN.
"THE THREE KINDS OF TREASURE".
MAJ. WRITINGS, VOL. 2.

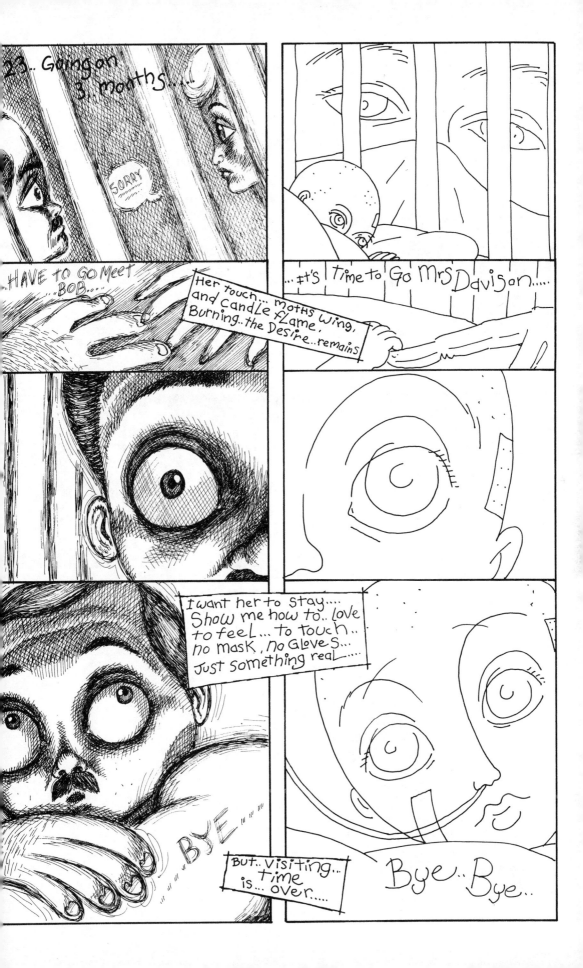

NOV, 1989, ON MY WAY TO VISIT MAGGIE

FUNNY HOW I'VE CHANGED SO MUCH, SINCE MAGGIE AND I GOT TOGETHER... I WAS LIKE A MIRROR WITHOUT A REFLECTION, DESPERATE FOR LOVE.

STRANGE LOOKING AT THESE EARLIER PAGES... DESPERATE, AND HOW!

IT TOOK SOME TIME BEFORE I REALISED THAT THE PROBLEM WAS THE 'DESPERATION' ITSELF... AND ALSO THAT, REALISING THAT, WAS ONLY THE START... DOING SOMETHING ABOUT IT... WAS THE REAL BATTLE... BUT MORE ON THAT A BIT LATER ON....

FUNNY THINGS AUTOBIOGRAPHIES... YOU START IT TO RECORD EVENTS IN YOUR LIFE... AND THE PROCESS, BECOMES AN EVENT IN IT-SELF, CAPABLE OF TRANSFORMING YOUR PERCEPTIONS OF THOSE PREVIOUS EVENTS AND EVEN YOUR LIFE, ITSELF...

THE NEXT TWO PAGES, I DREW A FEW YEARS BACK... PRE-MAGGIE, WHAT A CONTRAST... I STILL GET A KNOT IN MY STOMACH.....

ALSO CORRESPONDING PAGES, CHAPTER 4.

ON THE BRIDGE..THINKING OF JENNY...TRYING TO REMEMBER A HAPPIER ENDING...
SABOTAGED BY THOUGHTS OF CHILDHOOD FEAR, REALISED I HADN'T OUTGROWN LONELINESS
I'D JUST STOPPED LOOKING IT IN THE EYE.....

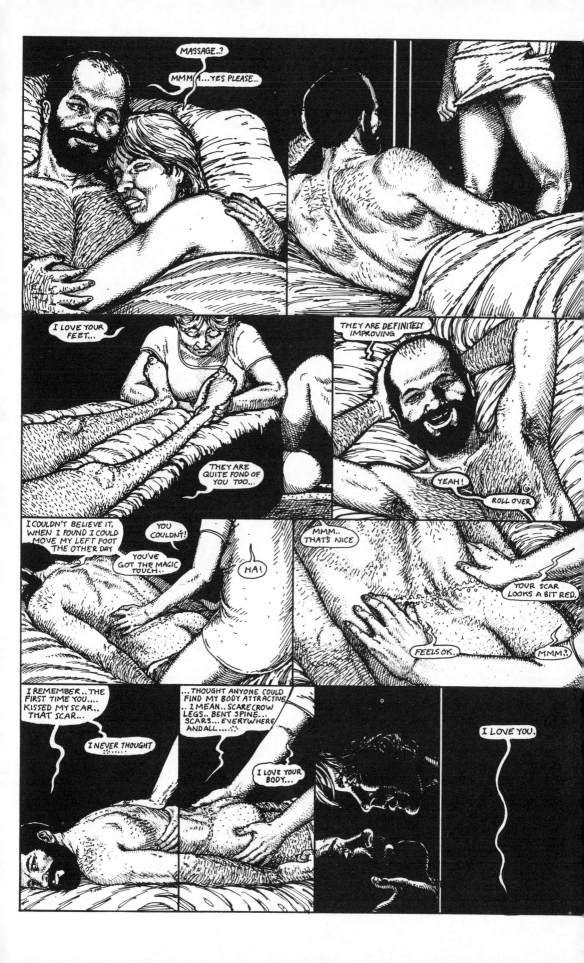

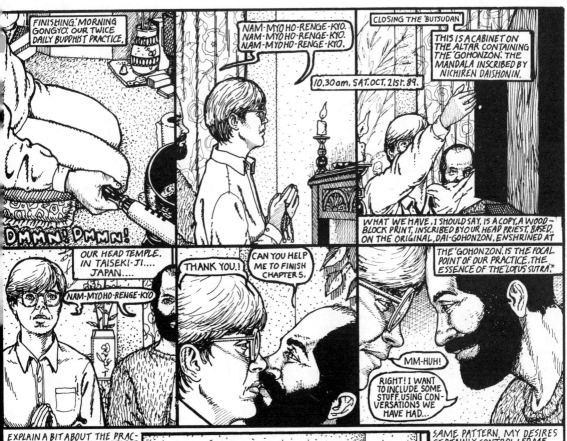

FINISHING. MORNING GONGYO. OUR TWICE DAILY BUDDHIST PRACTICE.

DMMN! DMMN!

NAM-MYOHO-RENGE-KYO. NAM-MYOHO-RENGE-KYO. NAM-MYOHO-RENGE-KYO.

10.30am, SAT. OCT. 21st. 89.

CLOSING THE 'BUTSUDAN'

THIS IS A CABINET ON THE ALTAR CONTAINING THE 'GOHONZON', THE MANDALA INSCRIBED BY NICHIREN DAISHONIN.

WHAT WE HAVE, I SHOULD SAY, IS A COPY, A WOOD-BLOCK PRINT, INSCRIBED BY OUR HEAD PRIEST, BASED ON THE ORIGINAL, DAI-GOHONZON, ENSHRINED AT

OUR HEAD TEMPLE. IN TAISEKI-JI.... JAPAN.... NAM-MYOHO-RENGE-KYO

THANK YOU!

CAN YOU HELP ME TO FINISH CHAPTER 5.

THE 'GOHONZON' IS THE FOCAL POINT OF OUR PRACTICE, THE ESSENCE OF THE 'LOTUS SUTRA.'*

MM-HUH!

RIGHT! I WANT TO INCLUDE SOME STUFF, USING CONVERSATIONS WE HAVE HAD...

EXPLAIN A BIT ABOUT THE PRACTICE... Y'NO, HOW SOME PEOPLE SEE BUDDHISM AS ALL SHAVED HEADS... RULES.. VERY AUSTERE, ERADICATION OF OUR DESIRES... NIRVANA... ETC.

"OK, 'EARTHLY DESIRES ARE ENLIGHTENMENT,' IS A GOOD START, IT SAYS HOW RATHER THAN TRYING TO ERADICATE OUR DESIRES, WE USE THEM CREATIVELY THEY ARE THE 'FUEL FOR THE FIRE', TO TRANSFORM OUR NEGATIVE KARMA."

"YEAH, THIS BUDDHISM IS ABOUT BEING WHOLE, NOT TRYING TO DENY OUR DESIRES OR ERADICATE THEM, BUT ACKNOWLEDGE THEM, TRANSFORM THEM, SO THEY DO NOT CONTROL US, BUT WORK TO HELP US EXPAND OUR LIVES."

"YES, ANGER, HUNGER, HELL, ETC... ALL HAVE POSITIVE SIDES TO THEM."

"HA, HA! YES... REMEMBER HOW WE GOT TOGETHER, I WAS GOING THROUGH HELL COZ I THOUGHT I WAS IN LOVE WITH A GOOD FRIEND OF MINE, AND SHE DIDN'T FEEL THE SAME WAY.. BUT IT WAS.. WELL LIKE I WAS FALLING FOR ANY WOMAN WHO SHOWED ME ANY AFFECTION... IT WAS SO NEW TO ME, I OVER-REACTED.. OF COURSE I HAD CLOSE FRIENDSHIPS.. BUT WOMEN-FRIENDS, WHO WANTED TO HOLD MY HAND AND HUG ME, WAS A NEW EXPERIENCE... AND I HAD LITTLE TO COMPARE WITH, I WASN'T SURE WHERE THE LINE WAS BETWEEN FRIENDSHIP AND A RELATIONSHIP, WASN'T CLEAR ON THOSE THINGS I FELT MOST PEOPLE UNDERSTOOD, WHEN I LOOK BACK TO EARLIER SITUATIONS NOW, I CAN SEE... THEY ALL FOLLOWED THAT

JUST ONE THING BOTHERING ME THO'...

WHAT'S THAT HONEY?

WELL THIS IS THE END OF CHAPTER FIVE..

SO...

SAME PATTERN, MY DESIRES CERTAINLY CONTROLLED ME... CONFUSED ME... BUT BACK TO THIS SITUATION, THIS FRIEND, RATHER THAN REJECT ME OUTRIGHT, JUST CONTINUED TO ENCOURAGE ME TO KEEP CHANTING, AND SHE"...

"HA, HA! YES! SHE TOLD YOU THE QUOTE, ABOUT THE ROAD TO KYOTO, TAKING TWELVE DAYS, AND IF YOU STOPPED ON THE ELEVENTH DAY, YOU WOULD NEVER SEE THE MOON OVER THE CAPITAL."

"YEAH, LIKE SHE KNEW SOMETHING I DIDN'T.. WHICH OF COURSE SHE DID, SHE ALSO KNEW I WAS TOO CLOSE TO THE SITUATION TO HEAR WHAT SHE WAS SAYING... SHE SAID I SHOULD PHONE SOMEONE I COULD TALK TOO... WHO DID I PHONE?.. YOU!! AND WHAT WAS THE FIRST THING YOU SAID WHEN YOU SAW ME?!" THE ROAD FROM KAMAKURA TO KYOTO TAKES TWELVE DAYS..." "IF YOU".. HA, HA! THIS, I DIDN'T WANT TO HEAR, THEN YOU CHANTED WITH ME, ALOT! I'D GOT SO WORKED UP I'D SPARKED OFF THE M.E. AGAIN, YOU NURSED ME, CHANTED WITH ME, AND LISTENED TO ME.. BY THE END OF THE WEEK, I UNDERSTOOD WHAT SHE, AND ALL MY FRIENDS HAD KNOWN, AND WAS ABLE TO PUT THINGS INTO PERSPECTIVE.. A MONTH.. LATER WE WERE ABLE TO ACKNOWLEDGE OUR FEELINGS, I'D CHANGED ALOT.. EVEN SO YOU KNEW WE WERE HAVING A RELATIONSHIP BEFORE I DID. HA, I HAD STILL A WAY TO GO....

HOW DO I FIT ALL THIS INTO THREE PAGES?...

* THE HIGHEST TEACHING IN BUDDHISM.

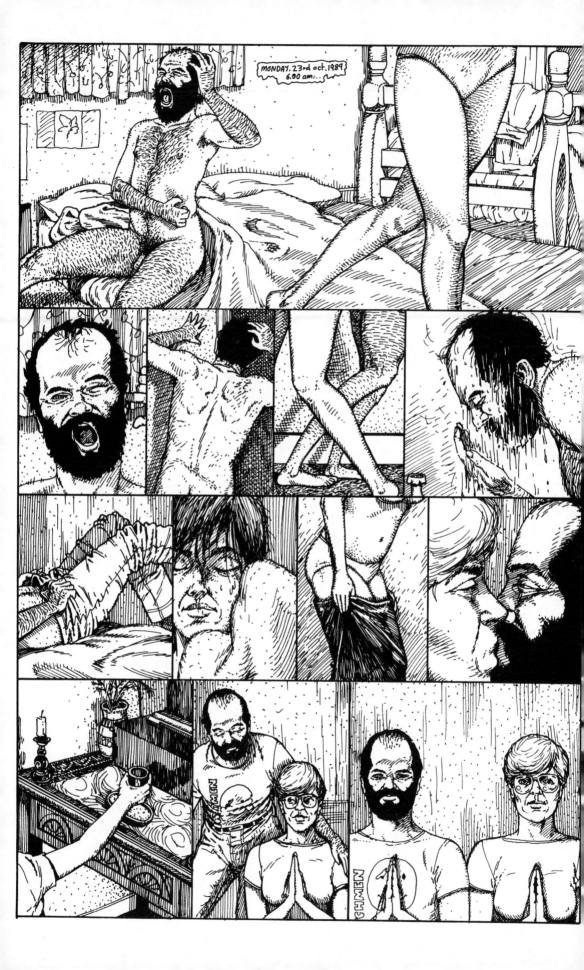

This book is respectfully dedicated to
Paula and Celia
friends who helped me discover
'the treasures of the heart'
and especially to
MAGGIE LAWRENCE
who is so generously sharing
those treasures with me